MISSION PARIS

Author: Catherine Aragon • Designers: Matteo Ciccarone, Nada Orlic (Cover)
Editor: Sue Peterson

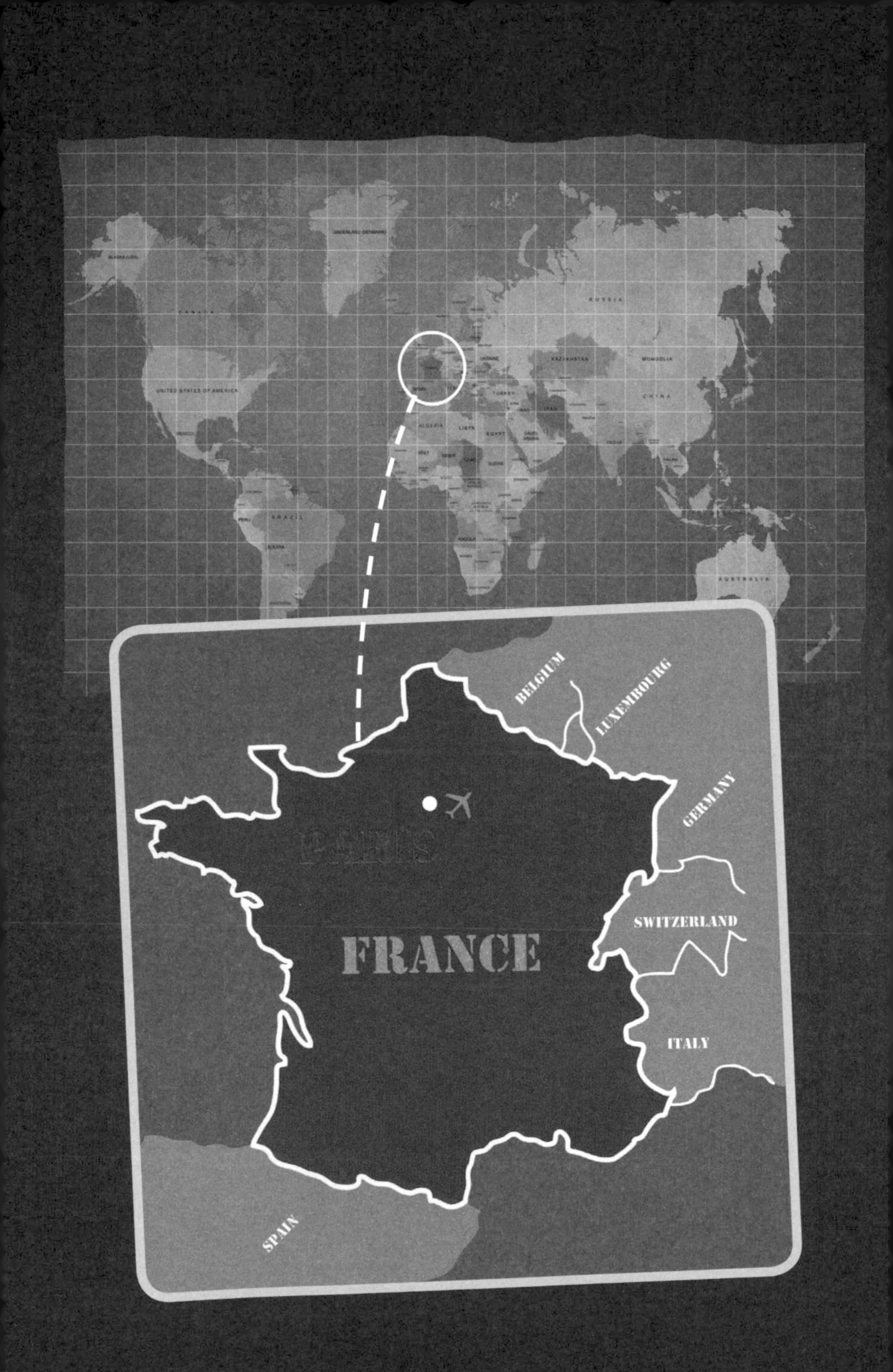
RUSSIA
CANADA
UNITED STATES OF AMERICA
KAZAKHSTAN
MONGOLIA
CHINA
BRAZIL
AUSTRALIA
BELGIUM
LUXEMBOURG
GERMANY
PARIS
FRANCE
SWITZERLAND
ITALY
SPAIN

CONTENTS

MISSION NUMBER		MISSION NAME	PAGE NUMBER	POINT VALUE	MY POINTS
		MISSION INFO + BONUS MISSION	2		
		MISSION RULES	3		
A	☐	PRE-ARRIVAL BRIEF	4	4	
1	☐	NOTRE DAME	6	31	
2	☐	PALAIS ROYAL	14	6	
3	☐	LOUVRE	18	26+	
4	☐	LOUVRE COUR CARRÉE	28	5	
5	☐	TUILERIES GARDENS	29	4	
6	☐	CHAMPS-ÉLYSÉES	30	8	
7	☐	TROCADÉRO	32	8	
8	☐	EIFFEL TOWER	36	9	
9	☐	CATACOMBS	38	7	
10	☐	LUXEMBOURG GARDENS	42	7	
11	☐	SACRÉ COEUR	46	10	
12	☐	CHÂTEAU DE VINCENNES	48	8	
13	☐	CITÉ DES ENFANTS	50	3	
14	☐	POMPIDOU CENTER	51	7	
15	☐	SAINTE CHAPELLE	52	13	
16	☐	MUSÉE D'ORSAY	54	17+	
17	☐	ANYTIME MISSIONS	56	13+	
		THE FINAL MISSION	61		

AFTER COMPLETING EACH MISSION CHECK (√) THE BOX AND WRITE THE NUMBER OF POINTS EARNED

AT THE END, WRITE THE TOTAL NUMBER OF POINTS HERE: ☐

ATTENTION: FUTURE SPECIAL AGENTS [YOU] AND CASE OFFICERS [GROWNUPS]

CONGRATULATIONS! THE SIA (SECRET INTERNATIONAL AGENCY) HAS SELECTED YOU AS A CANDIDATE TO BECOME A SPECIAL AGENT.

The SIA carries out important assignments, secretly collecting intelligence in all corners of the globe. ("Intelligence" is spy-speak for "information.") Currently, we are in dire need of agents. Many want to join us, but only a few have what it takes.

HOW WILL YOU PROVE YOU'RE READY TO JOIN THE MOST ELITE SPY AGENCY IN THE WORLD? You must complete a series of missions in Paris, France, where you'll venture to ancient monuments, colossal castles, mysterious bell towers, and spooky underground tunnels. Similar to a scavenger hunt (only better), these missions will require you to carry out challenging investigations and collect valuable intel (short for "intelligence"). For each mission, you'll earn points towards becoming a special agent.

YOUR ASSIGNMENT: TRAVEL TO PARIS WITH YOUR TEAM, LED BY YOUR CASE OFFICER. (A case officer accompanies agents on missions. Your case officer is your parent or other trusted adult.) You must earn at least 100 points to become a SIA special agent.

-The list of missions and mission scorecard are on page 1.

-Read the "Anytime Missions" early, so that you'll remain on alert and ready to earn points. You can complete these at any time during your stay.

-You don't need to complete all of the missions listed to reach 100 points or complete them in any particular order.

-The answer key is on page 60.

Want even more Paris fun? Visit **Scavengerhuntadventures.Com/bonus** (all lowercase) today to download your **free bonus mission: "ARAGO MEDALLIONS."**

(Plus, you'll get *The Museum Spy*, our free e-book!)

"Get Your Bonus Mission Today!"

MISSION RULES

- Be kind and respectful to team members.
- Your case officer (your parent or other trusted adult) has the final decision regarding point awards.
- Your case officer serves as the official "scorekeeper."
- Your case officer has the final decision on what missions will be attempted. (Don't worry, you can still earn enough points to become an agent without completing all the missions.)
- Always be on alert. You never know when a chance to earn points lies just around the corner.

TO CONCEAL THEIR REAL IDENTITIES, SPECIAL AGENTS ALWAYS USE CODE NAMES. FOR EXAMPLE, JAMES BOND'S CODE NAME IS 007. THINK OF YOUR OWN CODE NAME TO USE DURING YOUR MISSION IN PARIS.

SIGN YOUR CODE NAME HERE:

....

____

DATE

IMPORTANT: FOR THE MISSIONS YOU WILL NEED A PEN OR PENCIL AND A CAMERA.

PARIS PRE-ARRIVAL BRIEF

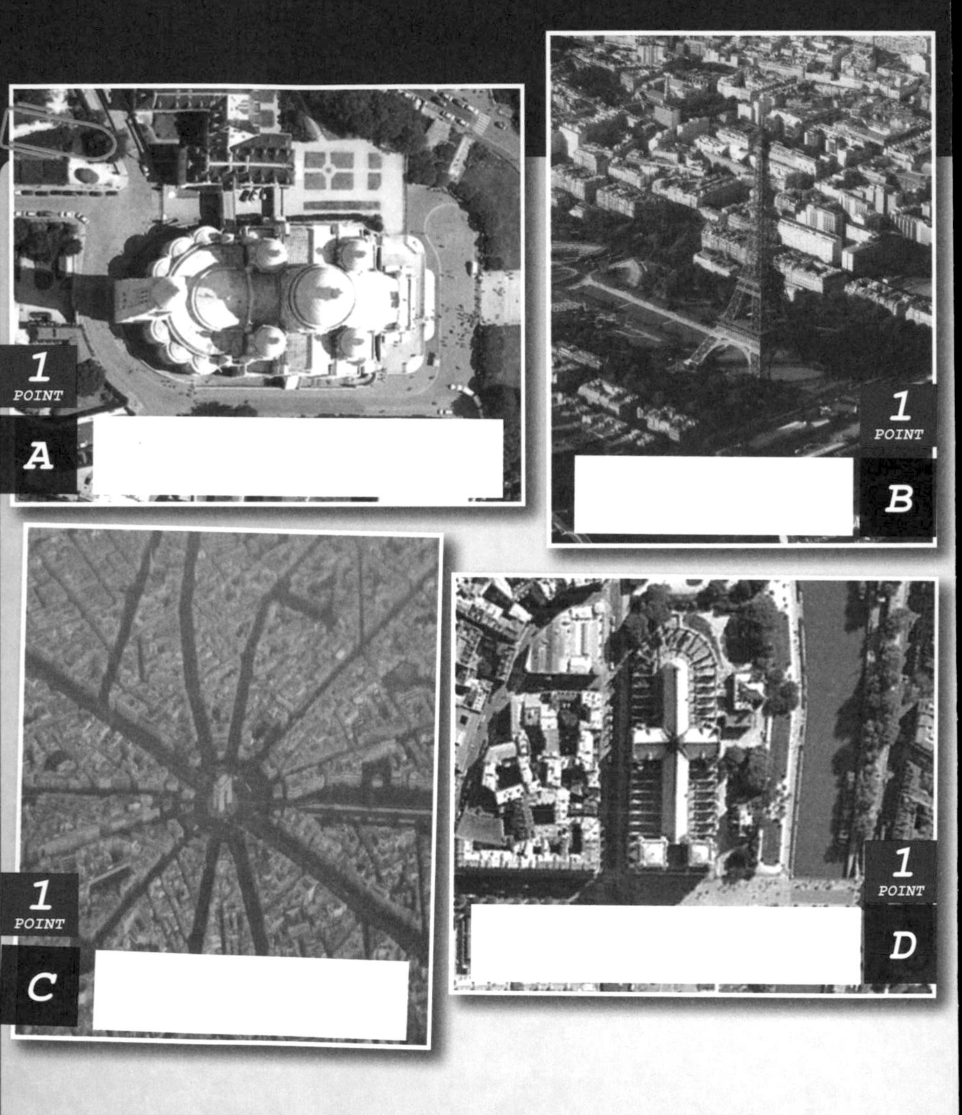

AGENTS MUST HAVE SHARP SKILLS WHEN IT COMES TO ANALYZING IMAGES, SUCH AS PHOTOGRAPHS, IN ORDER TO GATHER IMPORTANT INTEL. AERIAL PHOTOS LIKE THESE ARE TAKEN FROM HIGH IN THE SKY, FROM A PLANE, HELICOPTER, OR SKYSCRAPER.

my notes:

First, examine these aerial photos of Paris monuments. Next, study the photos of the same monuments taken at ground-level. (below)

USING THE GROUND-LEVEL PHOTO AND THE MONUMENT'S DESCRIPTION, WRITE WHAT MONUMENT APPEARS IN EACH AERIAL PHOTO ON PAGE 4.

1)NOTRE DAME

2)EIFFEL TOWER

3)SACRÉ COEUR

4)ARC DE TRIOMPHE

- **NOTRE DAME** *("No-truh Dahm")*
  - The largest cathedral (church) in Paris
  - Shaped like a cross
- **EIFFEL TOWER** *("Eye-full")*
  - Most famous monument of Paris
  - Tall tower
- **SACRÉ COEUR** *("Sak-ray Kuhr")*
  - Sometimes called the "white castle" (even though it's a church)
- **ARC DE TRIOMPHE** *("Ark duh Tree-omf")*
  - A large arch at the center of a world-famous round-about
  - Twelve avenues meet here, at a place called "Étoile" ("Ay-twal").
  - "Étoile" means "star." From above, the area resembles a star.

(Notre Dame = "No-truh Dahm")

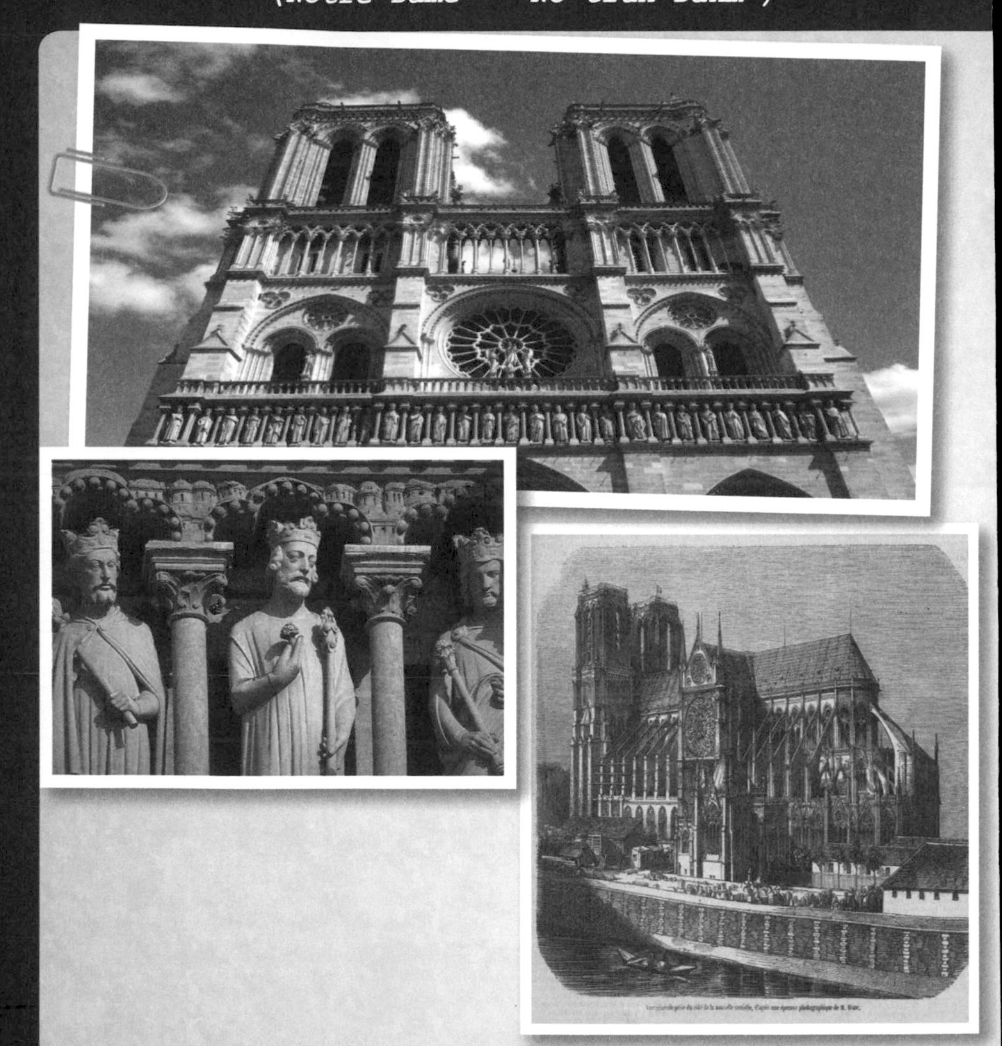

Ever heard of *The Hunchback of Notre Dame*, the story of the hunch-backed man, Quasimodo, who rang cathedral bells all day and fell in love with the beautiful gypsy, Esmeralda? Well, this is the cathedral where the story took place.

31

TOTAL POINTS

- CLIMB THE BELL TOWER
- GARGOYLE WITH GRAPES
- GARGOYLE PHOTO
- EMMANUEL BELL
- VIEW FROM THE TOWER
- NATIONAL SYMBOL
- NEW DESIGN
- POINT ZERO
- BIBLICAL KINGS
- SAINT DENIS
- PIGEONS
- ROSE WINDOW
- STAINED GLASS
- JOAN OF ARC

THE BELL TOWER

AS A SPECIAL AGENT, YOU MUST BE IN TIP-TOP SHAPE.

If you're up for a challenge, then get ready for a hike!

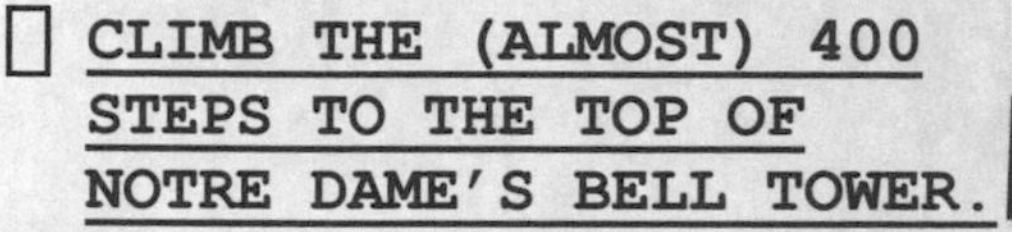

☐ **CLIMB THE (ALMOST) 400 STEPS TO THE TOP OF NOTRE DAME'S BELL TOWER.**

3 POINTS

From the tower, you have a close-up view of some creepy gargoyles. When Notre Dame was built around 800 years ago, people believed these gargoyles kept evil spirits away from the cathedral. In addition to warding off ghosts and goblins, they served as drain spouts. When it rained, the rain water drained off the cathedral roof, into rain gutters, and then gushed out through the gargoyles.

☐ **FIND THE GARGOYLE MUNCHING ON SOME GRAPES.** *2 POINTS*

☐ **LOCATE THE SCARIEST GARGOYLE, AND HAVE YOUR PHOTO TAKEN IMITATING THE EXPRESSION ON ITS FACE.** *2 POINTS*

(If there's not enough space or light to take the photo in the tower, you can do this outside too. You'll find gargoyles all around the cathedral.)

my notes:

Check out the huge bells Quasimodo rang in *The Hunchback of Notre Dame*. The largest of all, the Emmanuel Bell, weighs 13 tons (that's about the same weight as 8 cars). The Emmanuel Bell rings only on special occasions. While exploring Notre Dame you may be lucky enough to hear the other bells ring. They mark the time of day and serve as a call to prayer.

2 POINTS ☐ **FIND THE 13-TON EMMANUEL BELL IN THE TOWER.**

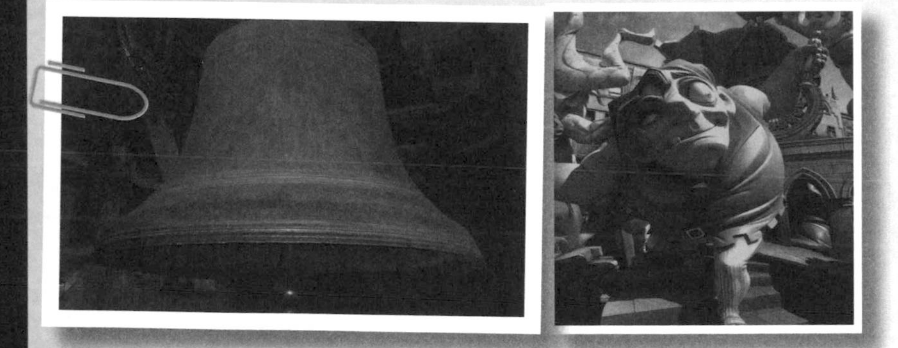

AGENTS MUST HAVE SHARP EYES TO SPOT THINGS FROM A DISTANCE. IN THE FIELD, SOMETIMES YOU CAN'T DEPEND ON ZOOM LENSES OR BINOCULARS FOR ASSISTANCE, JUST YOUR OWN TWO EYES.

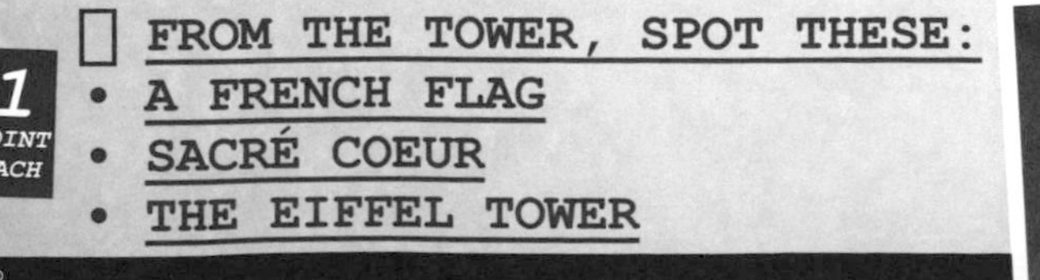

1 POINT EACH ☐ **FROM THE TOWER, SPOT THESE:**

- **A FRENCH FLAG**
- **SACRÉ COEUR**
- **THE EIFFEL TOWER**

my notes:

Important Note: Some tasks may not be possible due to repair work. (Use "Anytime Missions: Bonus" to "make up" the points.)

In April 2019, a terrible fire destroyed the cathedral's spire and roof. Examine the cathedral, and you'll see lots of stone...not exactly fire-prone material. The roof's frame, however, was made of wood (from 5,000 oak trees). The roof and spire collapsed, but the copper rooster (below) at the tip-top, a symbol of France, was spared and discovered after the fire.

☐ **DURING YOUR TRIP, FIND A SOUVENIR OR A SOCCER JERSEY WITH THIS NATIONAL SYMBOL.**

1 *POINT*

Currently, a competition is underway for the best design for a new spire/roof.

☐ **TO WIN THE PRIZE, HOW WOULD YOU DESIGN A NEW ROOF & SPIRE?**

3 *POINTS*

(Modern? "Gothic" like the rest of the cathedral? Or, a combo?)

OUTSIDE THE CATHEDRAL

In the square in front of Notre Dame lies a round stone marker on the ground with the words "Point Zero." Stand on the marker, and you'll be standing at the official center of Paris.

☐ **LOCATE POINT ZERO.**

From the square, examine the front of the cathedral. Among all the statues and sculptures, find those forming a row above the three doorways.

These are kings from the Bible.

2 *POINTS* ☐ **HOW MANY BIBLICAL KINGS ARE STANDING IN A ROW?**

my notes:

During the French Revolution (from 1787 to 1799), the citizens of France were completely fed up with the monarchy. The kings, queens, and royalty were living the high life while everyday people suffered. So, the citizens overthrew the monarchy.

The statues of these biblical kings were mistaken for statues of the kings of France. An angry mob tore them down and chopped off their heads! Then, in the middle of the night, a Parisian who had witnessed the "beheading" snuck to Notre Dame and gathered the heads of the poor kings. He returned to his home, dug a hole in his yard, and buried them for safe-keeping.

The heads remained hidden underground for nearly 200 years. Then, in 1977, on April 1, someone finally discovered them. Note the date: April 1. When the Paris authorities were informed of the discovery, they couldn't believe it. They thought it was an April Fools' joke.

(What we see today are replicas of the original heads, which are in a museum.)

Speaking of beheadings…on the left side of the left door, find a row of four statues. Notice anything strange about one of them?

☐ FIND THE STATUE WHO'S HOLDING HIS OWN HEAD (SAINT DENIS).

2 POINTS

Saint Denis was the city's first bishop. Back in the 3rd century Denis got in big trouble in his attempt to spread Christianity. The city's rulers didn't believe in Christianity, so they arrested Denis. Then they beheaded him. Legend has it that immediately afterwards Denis managed to kneel down, pick up his own head, and walk a few miles to the edge of Paris before calling it quits.

2 POINTS

☐ FEED THE PIGEONS OUTSIDE OF THE CATHEDRAL.

Although the French sometimes call pigeons "flying rats," believe it or not these birds served as spies during World Wars I and II. Today we sometimes use satellites to spy on enemies. Satellites orbit the Earth taking pictures. Back in the early 1900's satellites didn't exist, so something else had to be used that could fly high and secretly snap photos: specially-trained birds. **MILITARIES USED SPY PIGEONS THAT WOULD FLY ABOVE ENEMY ZONES WITH CAMERAS STRAPPED TO THEIR CHESTS**. The birds returned home with a camera full of photos with valuable intelligence.

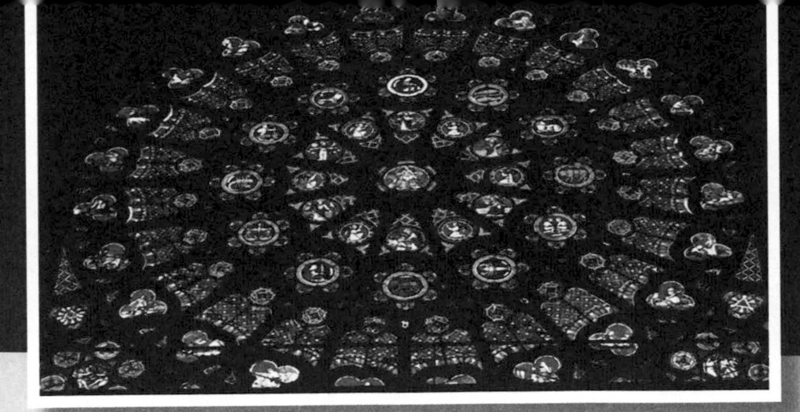

INSIDE THE CATHEDRAL

When you go inside, keep a lookout (and up) for "rose windows" - the large, round, multi-color stained glass windows.

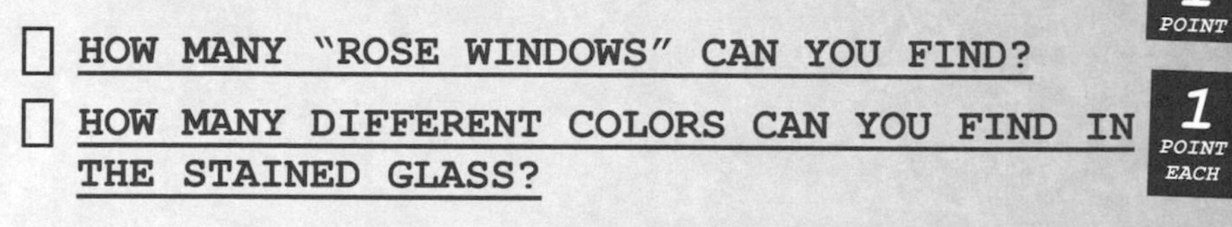

- ☐ **HOW MANY "ROSE WINDOWS" CAN YOU FIND?** *1 POINT*
- ☐ **HOW MANY DIFFERENT COLORS CAN YOU FIND IN THE STAINED GLASS?** *1 POINT EACH*

(1 point for each color, 4 points maximum)

Hunt down the statue of Joan of Arc, a warrior and a heroine of France. She is dressed in armor and praying. When Joan was only a teenager, France's king put her in charge of entire armies. At age 18, she led the army of France to victory against the British.

- ☐ **FIND THE STATUE OF JOAN OF ARC.** *2 POINTS*

(Palais= "Pa-lay")

THE PEOPLE WHO MAKE THE BEST SPIES ARE THOSE THAT YOU WOULD NEVER EVER SUSPECT OF SPYING IN THE FIRST PLACE.

They may appear to simply go about their daily lives, perhaps as a student, teacher, or doctor, but they're actually serving as undercover agents.

One of history's greatest spymasters, France's CARDINAL RICHELIEU *("Rish-a-loo")*, resided in the grand Palais Royal.

6

- BLACK AND WHITE COLUMNS PHOTO
- REFLECTING SPHERES PHOTO
- MINIATURE CANNON

TOTAL POINTS

In the 1600's Richelieu was head of France's Catholic Church. However, in the shadows he had another profession: the leader of one of the greatest spy networks of all time.

Richelieu had a complex web of agents stationed throughout the country, and they reported back to him the slightest hint of disloyalty. He had secret agents posted throughout the capitals of Europe, who spied on unsuspecting aristocrats*. The agents posed as fencing* instructors and dance teachers, all the while secretly collecting information about other nations' plots against France and then sending the valuable intelligence to their boss, Cardinal Richelieu.

IN THE 1980'S THE COURTYARD OF THE PALAIS ROYAL GOT A MAKEOVER - THE ADDITION OF 280 BLACK-AND-WHITE STRIPED COLUMNS. SOME PEOPLE LOVE THESE MODERN COLUMNS, WHILE OTHERS DESPISE THEM, DECLARING THAT THESE "PRISON STRIPE" COLUMNS CLASH WITH THE ELEGANT OLD PALACE. WHAT DO YOU THINK, LOVE 'EM OR HATE 'EM?

☐ **FIND THE COURTYARD WITH THE COLUMNS. STAND ON TOP ONE OF THE COLUMNS AND HAVE YOUR PICTURE TAKEN.**

2 POINTS

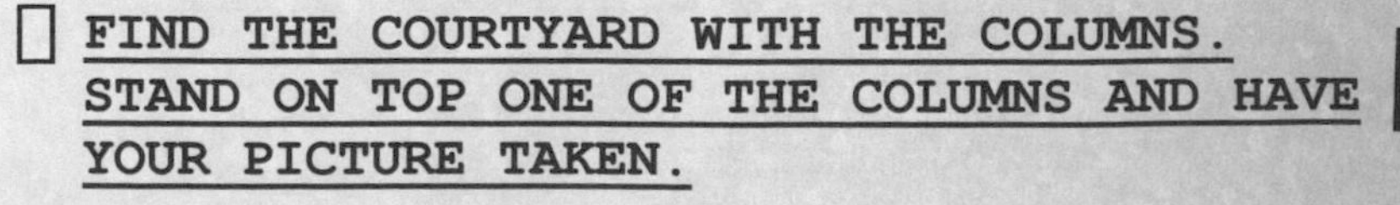

***"ARISTOCRAT"** = A MEMBER OF THE HIGHEST SOCIAL CLASS, OFTEN VERY WEALTHY AND POWERFUL ***"FENCING"** = SWORD FIGHTING

AS YOU KNOW, AGENTS MUST COLLECT DIFFERENT TYPES OF INTELLIGENCE. INTELLIGENCE COMES IN MANY FORMS, INCLUDING PHOTOS.

For this mission you need to take a photo of the Palais Royal, home to the famous spymaster, Cardinal Richelieu. The photo needs to be taken at a clever angle. Next to the courtyard, find the fountain with reflecting spheres.

2 POINTS ☐ **TAKE A PHOTO OF THE SPHERES WITH THE PALACE APPEARING IN THE REFLECTION. (LIKE IN THE PICTURE ABOVE)**

my notes:

Beside the courtyard are the palace gardens. On one of the lawns in the gardens, resting atop a stone mount, sits a miniature bronze cannon.

☐ **FIND THE MINIATURE CANNON IN THE GARDENS.** 

If you're here on a Wednesday around mid-day, be careful where you stand in the gardens because every Wednesday at noon this miniature cannon goes off...with smoke and all. The cannon here now is a replica of the original from the 1700's. Back then, people would use the cannon to set their clocks. Exactly at 12:00 every sunny day, almost like magic, the cannon would fire. The sun's rays were strongest at noon, so as they passed through the cannon's magnifying lens, they automatically lit the cannon's fuse, and

BOOM!

mission: #3 date:__________

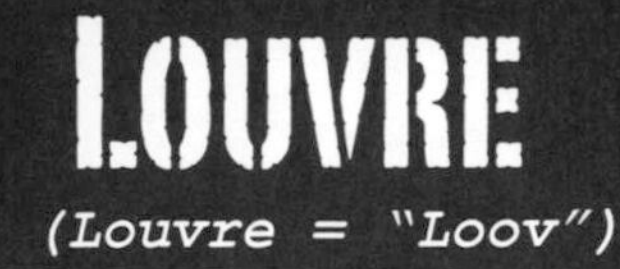

(Louvre = "Loov")

The Louvre, one of the world's largest museums, has so much art (35,000 works) it would take about 25 days - without sleeping - to see everything. Don't worry, you only have to venture into a few areas of the museum to complete this mission.

LOUVRE GLASS PYRAMIDS

Glass pyramids stand at the Louvre's main entrance. (Since the Louvre has a few different entrances, you may or may not have entered here.) Carefully count the number of glass pyramids at the entrance. **We emphasize carefully, because there's a trick to it. Don't miss the upside-down glass pyramid inside the museum's lobby.** Don't forget to include it in your final count.

TOTAL POINTS

- GLASS PYRAMIDS
- POSTCARDS
- CASTLE REPLICA
- CAT MUMMY
- SPHINX (2)
- SHEDU/LAMASSU (3)
- MONA LISA PHOTO
- WEDDING FEAST AT CANA
- CORONATION OF NAPOLEON
- THE CHEAT
- AUTUMN

☐ **FIND ALL THE LOUVRE'S GLASS PYRAMIDS AT THE MAIN ENTRANCE AREA (INCLUDING THE UPSIDE DOWN ONE).**

3 POINTS

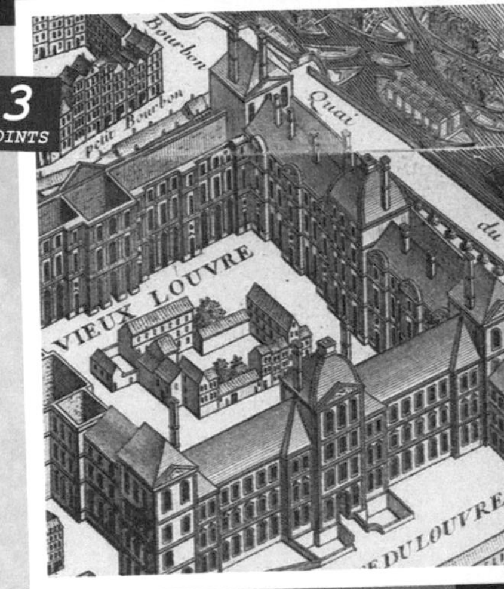

Before making your way into the exhibits, hunt down a gift shop with a postcard rack of the museum's works. Together with your case officer, pick out a few postcards of interesting items to find once inside. Your case officer sets the number of points per postcard.

☐ **FIND THE ARTWORK IN THE POSTCARDS.**

___ POINT(S) EACH

LOUVRE FOUNDATIONS

Before becoming a museum, the Louvre was a luxurious palace that France's royalty called home-sweet-home. And before that, on this same site rested a mighty medieval fortress. Its massive walls and tall towers protected all those who lived inside. Deep within the Louvre, in the museum's "basement," discover the remains of this old fortress.

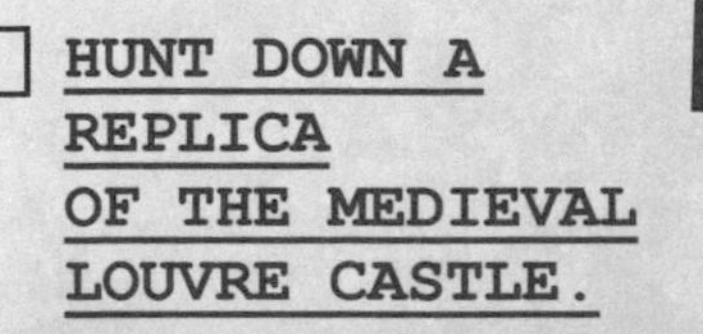

☐ **HUNT DOWN A REPLICA OF THE MEDIEVAL LOUVRE CASTLE.**

1 POINT

my notes:

EGYPTIAN ART

Ancient Egyptians believed that after dying, they would journey to a different world and begin another life. To keep the bodies of the dead in tip-top shape for this special trip and for a new life, they created mummies. The Egyptians believed in an after-life for animals too, so some even created mummies for their pets.

2 POINTS ☐ **TRACK DOWN A MUMMY OF A CAT.**

The ancient Egyptians worshipped the sphinx.

These statues, thousands of years old, are half-human, half-animal.

1 POINT ☐ **THE BODY OF A SPHINX IS WHAT ANIMAL?**

2 POINTS ☐ **LOCATE AN ANCIENT SPHINX.**

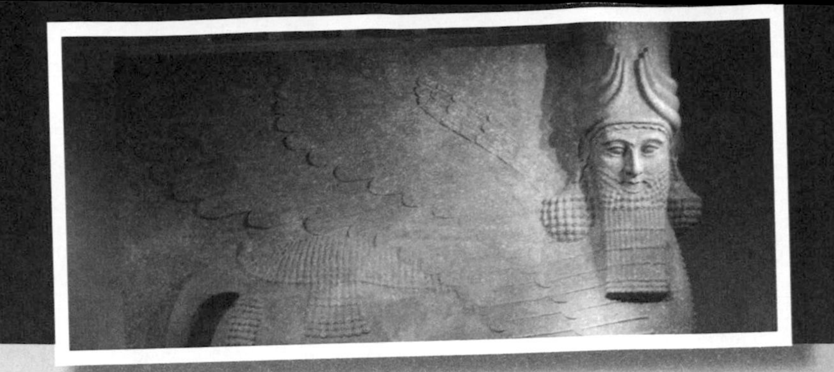

MESOPOTAMIA

In the ancient land of Mesopotamia archeologists uncovered even more half-human, half-animal statues. Called **"shedus"** *or* **"lamassus"** by the Mesopotamians, these creatures have human heads and bodies resembling a bull. They once proudly stood at city and palace gates, guarding against enemies.

- [ ] **FIND THE SHEDUS/LAMASSUS.**

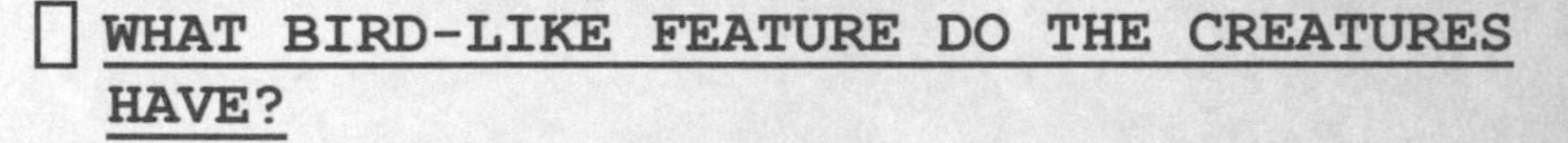

- [ ] **WHAT BIRD-LIKE FEATURE DO THE CREATURES HAVE?**

1
POINT

- [ ] **HOW MANY LEGS DO THE CREATURES HAVE?**

(Count the legs on an actual statue - not on the below image.)

mission: #3 date: __________

MONA LISA

Congratulations! Today, you join the ranks of about eight million people who see the *Mona Lisa* each year. Over 500 years ago the Italian artist, Leonardo da Vinci, created the *Mona Lisa*. Little did he know that his portrait of an Italian woman would become **the most famous painting in the world.**

☐ **HUNT DOWN THE WORLD'S MOST FAMOUS PAINTING AND SNAP A PHOTO OF IT.**

WHY EXACTLY IS THIS PARTICULAR PAINTING SO FAMOUS? IT ALL STARTED IN 1911 WHEN A THIEF MANAGED TO STEAL IT FROM THE LOUVRE. BACK THEN THE MUSEUM DIDN'T HAVE THE COUNTLESS VIDEO CAMERAS AND SECURITY GUARDS THAT PROTECT THE ART TODAY.

A man who worked at the museum, an Italian named Vincenzo Peruggia, pulled off the heist of the *Mona Lisa*. Peruggia believed that the painting belonged in Italy, where Leonardo da Vinci had originally created it.

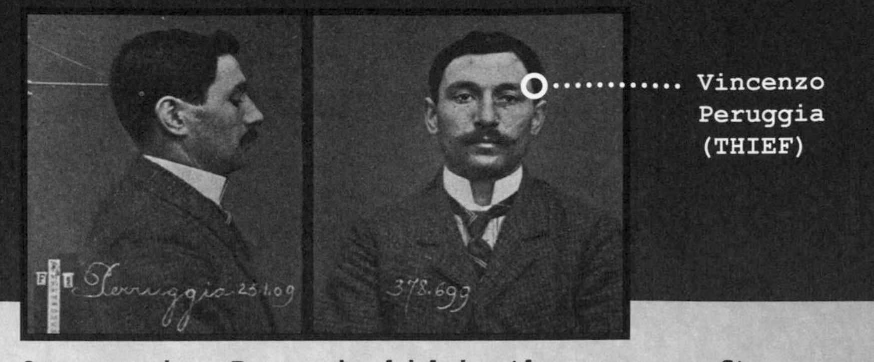

One evening Peruggia hid in the museum after closing time. He slipped into the room where the *Mona Lisa* **hung, quietly removed the painting from its frame, and tip-toed out of the museum with it hidden beneath his shirt. After creeping back to his apartment, he hid it in a false-bottom chest.**

There the *Mona Lisa* remained for two years as the police searched all around Paris. The police suspected Peruggia, and even questioned him about his whereabouts the night the painting vanished. Peruggia lied to the police, and even though the *Mona Lisa* thief sat right in front of them, they let him go.

Newspapers around the world splashed *Mona Lisa* photos across their pages, while the police hoped the painting would turn up somewhere. In Paris people lined up at the Louvre to simply gaze at the empty space on the wall where the painting once hung.

In 1913, Peruggia took the *Mona Lisa* back to its homeland. He brought the painting to an art gallery, expecting to receive a reward for returning it to Italy. Instead, the gallery's owner notified the police, and Peruggia ended up in the slammer.

FOLLOWING THIS THEFT THE LOUVRE HAS GUARDED THE MONA LISA CAREFULLY TO ENSURE THAT SOMETHING LIKE PERUGGIA'S HEIST NEVER HAPPENS AGAIN. INSTEAD OF STEALING PAINTINGS, NOWADAYS THIEVES (LIKE PICKPOCKETS) ARE MORE LIKELY TO SNATCH THE VALUABLES OF UNSUSPECTING VISITORS,

SO BE ON THE LOOKOUT!

mission: #3 date: ___________

my notes:

LOUVRE PAINTINGS

IT'S CRITICAL THAT YOU HAVE FIRST-RATE SKILLS IN IMAGE ANALYSIS.

Frequently agents have to carefully examine images, searching for small details that provide valuable clues. Let's put your skills to the test. With the assistance of your case officer or someone else in your team, track down these paintings.

THE WEDDING FEAST AT CANA

In the same room as the *Mona Lisa* hangs the Louvre's largest painting, *The Wedding Feast at Cana*.

1 POINT ☐ **FIND THREE DIFFERENT KINDS OF ANIMALS IN THE PAINTING.**

1 POINT ☐ **WHAT ANIMAL IS STANDING ON THE DINNER TABLE?**

THE CORONATION OF NAPOLEON

Napoleon Bonaparte, once the most powerful person in all of Europe, said, "Imagination rules the world." This idea may or may not be true. However, one thing is certain: Napoleon's imagination rules in this painting.

This huge work took almost two years for Napoleon's artist to complete. It shows Napoleon's coronation, the ceremony where he crowned himself Emperor of France in 1804. However, some of the most important parts present an inaccurate image of what happened. Napoleon created them from his imagination, and they're outright lies.

Napoleon wanted people seeing the painting (like you) to believe this event was perfect, so he made the artist change a few key details. Can you spot Napoleon's "lies?"

☐ **FIND NAPOLEON. HE'S THE MAN AT THE CENTER PLACING THE CROWN ON HIS WIFE'S HEAD.** **1 POINT**

In reality, Napoleon placed the crown on his own head. However, showing this would make him appear very selfish. Instead, the artist painted Napoleon placing it on his wife Josephine's head, making her empress.

☐ **FIND NAPOLEON'S MOTHER. LOOK FOR THE LARGE GOLD CROSS IN THE CENTER, THEN LOOK TO THE LEFT AND FIND THE WOMAN SITTING IN THE CHAIR.** **1 POINT**

my notes:

Napoleon's mother didn't even show up for his coronation. Poor Napoleon, she refused to attend because Napoleon had a serious argument with his brother.

1 POINT ☐ **FIND THE TWO WOMEN HOLDING THE EMPRESS JOSEPHINE'S CAPE.**

These two women, Josephine's attendants, were people of Napoleon's imagination. Check out their expressions - they look content. However, the real women who held Josephine's cape probably had angry scowls. These two attendants from the painting didn't hold Josephine's cape: Napoleon's sisters did. These sisters despised appearing like servants to Napoleon's wife as they held her train to keep it off the floor. They held Josephine's cape only after Napoleon ordered them to do so.

THE CHEAT WITH THE ACE OF DIAMONDS

Track down this painting showing a cardshark hiding the ace behind his back, waiting until the perfect moment to switch it into his other hand, throw his cards down onto the table and claim the pile of gold coins as his own. Compare the painting on the next page with the original.

3 POINTS ☐ **FIND FIVE ITEMS ADDED TO THIS THAT ARE NOT IN THE ORIGINAL.**

AUTUMN

Take a closer look at this work and you'll see a "man" made of fruit, vegetables, grains, wood…did we miss anything? Just as you did with *The Cheat*, compare the following work with the original.

3 POINTS ☐ **UNCOVER FIVE ITEMS ADDED TO THIS THAT ARE NOT IN THE ORIGINAL.**

THE CHEAT WITH THE ACE OF DIAMONDS

AUTUMN

mission: #4 date: ____________

LOUVRE COUR CARRÉE

(Cour Carrée = "Koor Kar-ay")

NOW WE'LL PUT YOUR MAP READING SKILLS TO THE TEST.

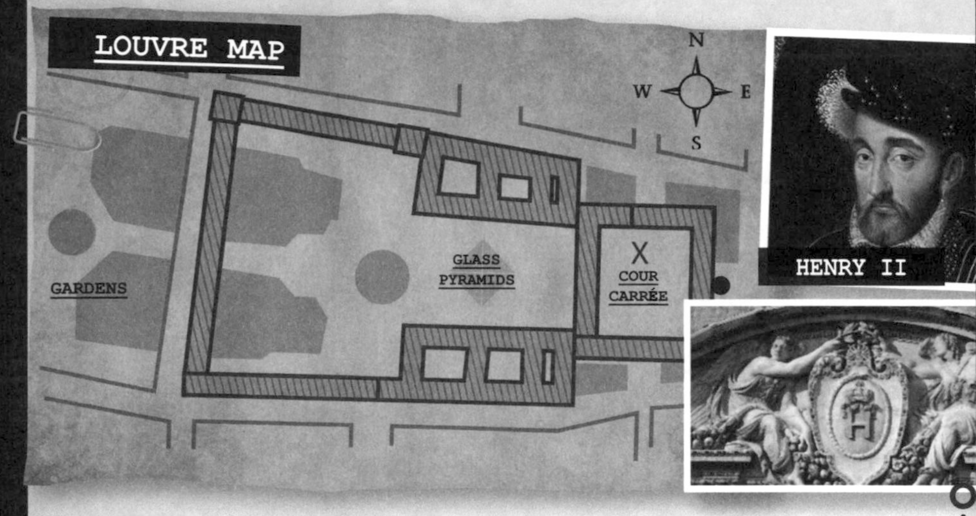

Using the map, trek to the center of the Louvre's Cour Carrée ("square courtyard") (the red "X"), which lies east of the glass pyramids.

Rulers left reminders of their reigns scattered around the Louvre. They rarely missed a chance to put initials on walls, gates, and above windows.

2 POINTS ☐ **FIND THIS SYMBOL OF KING HENRY II ABOVE A WINDOW.**

Venture under the archways to the sidewalk (marked with a blue dot). King Louis XVIII (XVIII = 18) certainly didn't want anyone to forget his reign.

3 POINTS ☐ **TRACK DOWN AT LEAST 20 DOUBLE L'S. (ꓶL)**

KING HENRY DIED BY THE SWORD IN A DUEL, LEAVING HIS 15-YEAR-OLD SON, FRANCIS, TO RULE FRANCE WITH HIS SCOTTISH WIFE, MARY. (SEE PAGE 44 FOR THE TRAGIC DETAILS OF MARY'S LIFE.)

mission: #5 date: __________

4

TOTAL POINTS

TUILERIES GARDENS

(Tuileries = "Twee-ler-ee")

THIS MISSION HAS TWO PARTS:

FIRST PART:

☐ **HUNT DOWN THE IN-GROUND TRAMPOLINES AND TAKE A TURN JUMPING UP, UP, AND UP.**

2 POINTS

(Note: Some people don't even know these trampolines exist because they're in the ground, not above the ground like most trampolines. Let your case officer know that they're near the Place de la Concorde *("Plas duh lah Kon-kord")* entrance, on the Rue de Rivoli *("Roo duh Reev-oh-lee")* side.)

SECOND PART:

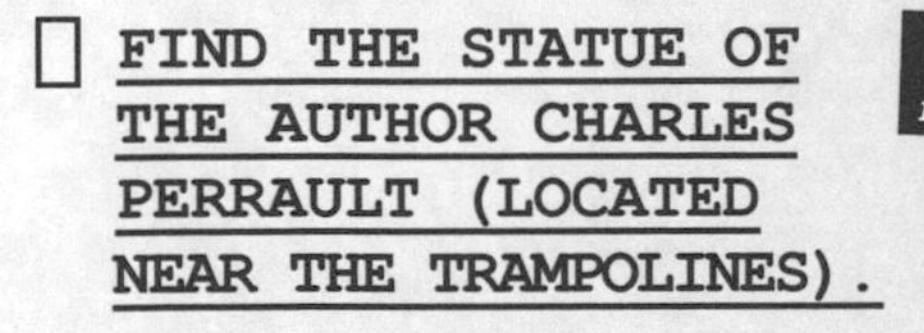

☐ **FIND THE STATUE OF THE AUTHOR CHARLES PERRAULT (LOCATED NEAR THE TRAMPOLINES).**

2 POINTS

Ever heard of this guy? Take a closer look at the photo - on the right side. That's not a child dressed in a cape and fancy hat, but a cat. Perhaps you've heard of this crafty cat. He's "Le Chat Botté" *("Luh Sha Bow-tay")*, "Puss in Boots."

Perrault *("Per-oe")* wrote the tale of *Puss in Boots* and some others you probably know - *Cinderella* and *Little Red Riding Hood*.

Champs-Élysées

(Champs-Élysées = "Shahns-Ay-Lee-Zay")

The Champs-Élysées starts at Place de la Concorde *("Plas duh lah Kon-kord")* (Concorde Square). Here, you'll find something shaped like a giant crayon - the Luxor Obelisk.

1 POINT ☐ **WHAT COLOR IS THE TOP OF THE OBELISK?**

The obelisk was brought to France all the way from Egypt, where it had stood at the entrance to the 3,000-year-old Luxor Temple. In the year 2000, a man known as France's Spiderman, Alain Robert *("Ah-lahn Roe-bare")*, managed to climb all the way to the top of the obelisk, using only his bare hands and climbing shoes.

8

- LUXOR OBELISK
- STREET SIGN
- CLIMB TO THE TOP OF THE ARC DE TRIOMPHE
- VIEW FROM THE TOP

TOTAL POINTS

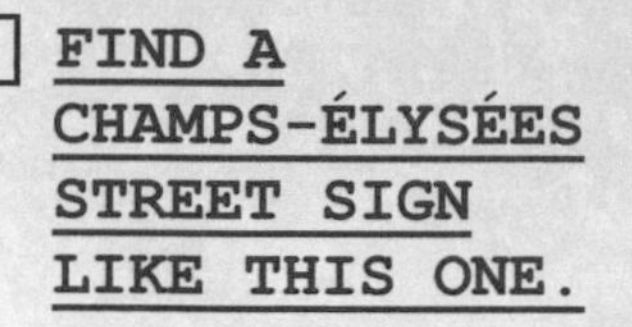

☐ **FIND A CHAMPS-ÉLYSÉES STREET SIGN LIKE THIS ONE.**

2 *POINTS*

(It has to be a real street sign, not a souvenir.)

At the end of the Champs-Élysées, you'll find the "Arc de Triomphe," *("Ark duh Tree-omf")* a monument to the people who fought and died for France in wars. You'll see a small memorial with a lighted flame (it's been burning since 1923) to remember the soldiers who died. Believe it or not, in 1919 a daredevil courageously flew a plane through the middle of the arch.

Here's another test of your physical strength:

☐ **CLIMB OVER 250 STEPS UP TO THE TOP OF THE ARC DE TRIOMPHE.**

3 *POINTS*

☐ **LOCATE THESE MONUMENTS FROM THE TOP:**
- **SACRÉ COEUR**
- **THE EIFFEL TOWER**

1 *POINT EACH*

mission: #7 date:___________

TROCADÉRO
AND THE BEST VIEW OF THE EIFFEL TOWER

(Trocadéro = "Trok-a-dare-o")

OK, now it's your turn. Are you up to the challenge of planning one of the most important missions of your trip (with a little assistance from your case officer)? It's up to you to get your team to Trocadéro for a picture-perfect view of Paris' most famous monument: the Eiffel Tower. The mission has two parts.

PART ONE:

2 POINTS ☐ **FIND THE TROCADÉRO MÉTRO STOP USING THE PARIS MÉTRO MAP.**

8

- FIND TROCADÉRO ON A MÉTRO MAP
- THE BEST VIEW OF THE EIFFEL TOWER
- EIFFEL TOWER PHOTO ILLUSION

TOTAL POINTS

• You will need a map of the Paris subway system. The subway system is called the Métro. (Your case officer probably has a Métro map.)

• The Paris Métro system consists of different stops along various lines. The lines each have their own number, color, and name.

• Using your case officer's map, on the left side in the center, look for the stop called "Trocadéro."

• Look on the left side of the map, and locate either Line 6 (a light green color) or Line 9 (a yellow-green color). Then, follow either of them until you find Trocadéro. The two lines cross at the Trocadéro stop.

• You can use either Line 6 or 9 to get to Trocadéro.

• Consult with your case officer and choose which of the two lines to use and to decide the best time to complete the second part of this mission.

my notes:

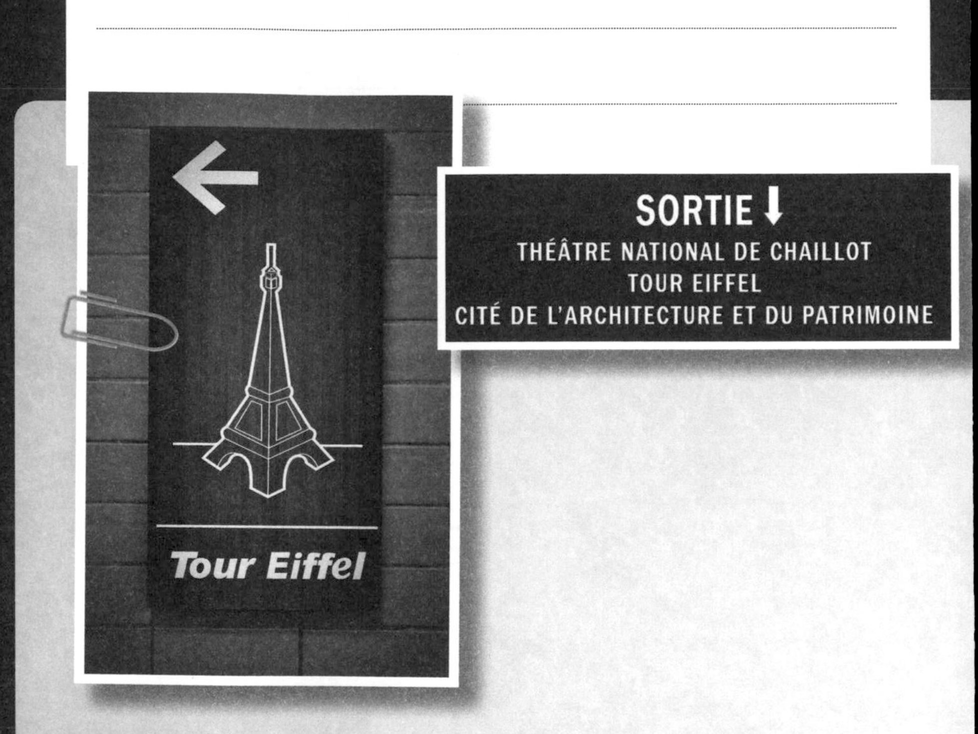

PART TWO:

3 POINTS ☐ DISCOVER THE BEST VIEW OF THE EIFFEL TOWER AT TROCADÉRO.

- After getting off the Métro at the Trocadéro station, follow the exit signs for "Tour Eiffel." (Tour Eiffel means Eiffel Tower.)

- Climb the steps up to the sidewalk.

- Continue walking forward and arrive at Trocadéro with a fantastic view of the Eiffel Tower.

AS YOU KNOW, IN THE WORLD OF SPECIAL AGENTS, THINGS AREN'T ALWAYS AS THEY SEEM. WHAT APPEARS TO BE AN ORDINARY PEN IS REALLY A VIDEO CAMERA. WHAT SEEMS TO BE AN ORDINARY KID VACATIONING IN PARIS IS REALLY A SECRET-AGENT-IN-TRAINING (YOU!).

The same goes for photographs: things aren't always as they appear. Take a look at this photo. It appears as if the man has fit the Eiffel Tower between his fingers.

To create this illusion, face the tower, hold up your thumb and index finger of your right hand in the shape of a "C." Have someone on your team stand next to you with a camera and have this person adjust your hand until the Eiffel Tower appears to fit between your fingers.

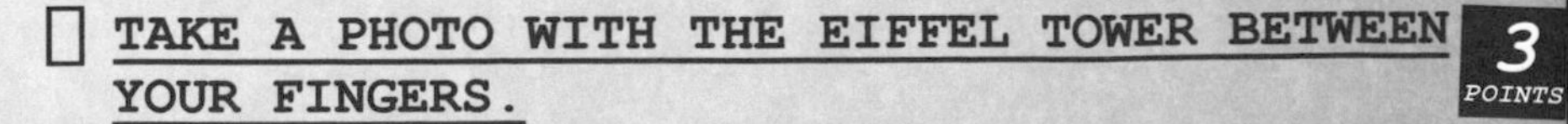

☐ **TAKE A PHOTO WITH THE EIFFEL TOWER BETWEEN YOUR FINGERS.** 3 POINTS

EIFFEL TOWER

Today, you'll become one of about seven million people who visit the Eiffel Tower each year.

The entire tower gets a new paint job every seven years, complete with its own patented Eiffel Tower brown color. Brave painters hang from the tower using special ropes, ensuring that every single step, beam, and bolt get a fresh coat.

When it's hot outside, the tower can "grow" up to six inches. The tower is made of iron, and when iron gets hot, it expands.

☐ **AT THE BASE OF THE TOWER, FIND THE GOLD BUST OF THE MAN WHO DESIGNED THE EIFFEL TOWER, GUSTAVE EIFFEL** *("Goo-stahv")*.

3 POINTS

AGENTS MUST HAVE EXCELLENT SURVEILLANCE SKILLS, WHETHER OBSERVING SOMEBODY OR SOMETHING. THIS MISSION WILL PUT YOUR SKILLS TO THE TEST FROM PARIS' TALLEST BUILDING.

9

- GUSTAVE EIFFEL BUST
- VIEW FROM THE TOWER
- EIFFEL'S OFFICE AND THE AMERICAN INVENTOR

TOTAL POINTS

AFTER MAKING YOUR WAY UP TO ONE OF THE TOWER'S OBSERVATION DECKS, LOCATE THESE:

1 POINT EACH

- **THE ARC DE TRIOMPHE**
- **NOTRE DAME CATHEDRAL**
- **A BOAT ON THE SEINE RIVER** *("Seine" = "Sen")*

At the top of the magnificent tower, Gustave Eiffel had his own office. From here he could enjoy a bird's eye view of Paris. Find his office, and inside you'll see the wax statues of Gustave Eiffel, Eiffel's daughter, and a friend of the Eiffels, an American inventor.

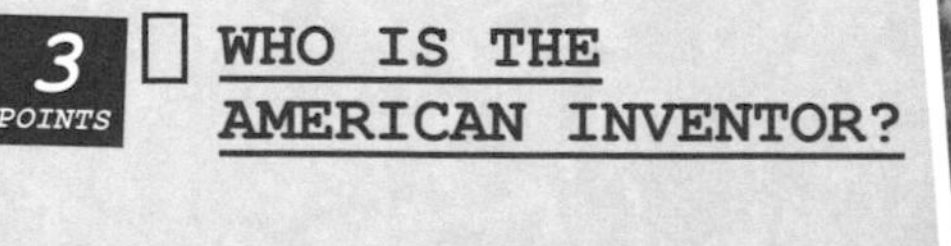

3 POINTS ☐ **WHO IS THE AMERICAN INVENTOR?**

CATACOMBS

Les Catacombes.

Paris is often called the "City of Light," but beneath the city a dark, spooky world exists: mazes of almost 200 miles of ancient tunnels, some of them filled with the bones of dead Parisians. One hundred and thirty steps below street level lie the catacombs of Paris.

ENTER THEM IF YOU DARE!

IN THESE TUNNELS LIE THE BONES OF SIX MILLION PARISIANS. BACK IN THE 18TH CENTURY, PARIS WASN'T SUCH A TIDY PLACE. BONES PILED UP IN CEMETERIES, AND NO SPACE REMAINED TO BURY THE DEAD. IN SOME CEMETERIES, SOIL MOUNDS REACHED 10 FEET ABOVE GROUND LEVEL. SO, UNDER THE COVER OF DARKNESS, CEMETERY WORKERS AND PRIESTS TRANSFERRED THE BONES HERE. THIS RITUAL CONTINUED FOR 70 YEARS, UNTIL 1859 WHEN THE FINAL BONES WERE LAID TO REST.

- "ENTRÉE DES CATACOMBES" SIGNS
- SCARY FACE PHOTO
- "ARRÊTE! C'EST ICI L'EMPIRE DE LA MORT" SIGN
- STONE PALACE

TOTAL POINTS

AGENTS MUST KEEP THEIR COOL AND ACCOMPLISH MISSIONS EVEN WHEN IN A DREADFUL PLACE (FOR EXAMPLE, IN TUNNELS FILLED WITH BONES). DO YOU HAVE THE STRENGTH TO CARRY OUT THIS MISSION DESPITE ITS LOCATION?

ABOVE GROUND

☐ **TRACK DOWN A SIGN THAT SAYS "ENTRÉE DES CATACOMBES."**

1 *POINT FOR EACH SIGN FOUND*

(*2 points max***)**

("Ahn-tray day Catacombs") (Catacomb Entrance) (Look up and down for signs.)

my notes:

mission: #9 date:__________

☐ **HAVE SOMEONE IN YOUR TEAM TAKE A PHOTO OF YOU MAKING YOUR BEST SCARY FACE!**

UNDER GROUND

2 POINTS

☐ **LOCATE THE SIGN OVER THE DOORWAY THAT SAYS, "ARRÊTE! C'EST ICI L'EMPIRE DE LA MORT."** *("Ah-ret Say tee-see lam-peer duh lah more") (Stop! Here lies the empire of death.)*

2 POINTS

☐ **FIND THE STONE CARVING OF THE PALACE.**

One of the catacomb's inspectors carved this palace. Unfortunately, this inspector died in the catacombs.

my notes:

This underground location has served as the perfect location for covert* meetings.

During World War II, when the German Nazis took control of France, members of the French Resistance snuck down into the catacombs to secretly plot against the Nazis. (The French Resistance "resisted" the Nazi invasion of their country.)

ONE OF THE GROUP'S MEMBERS AND ONE OF HISTORY'S MOST WELL-KNOWN SPIES WAS THE BEAUTIFUL ENTERTAINER JOSEPHINE BAKER. REMEMBER THAT THE PEOPLE WHO MAKE THE BEST SPIES ARE THOSE WHO YOU WOULD NEVER SUSPECT IN THE FIRST PLACE.

During the war, Nazi soldiers would attend Baker's performances, never suspecting that she, while singing and dancing, was actually listening to their conversations. She would even smuggle top secret intelligence across country lines using her sheet music, with the information written in invisible ink.

* COVERT = secret

mission: #10 date:__________

LUXEMBOURG GARDENS

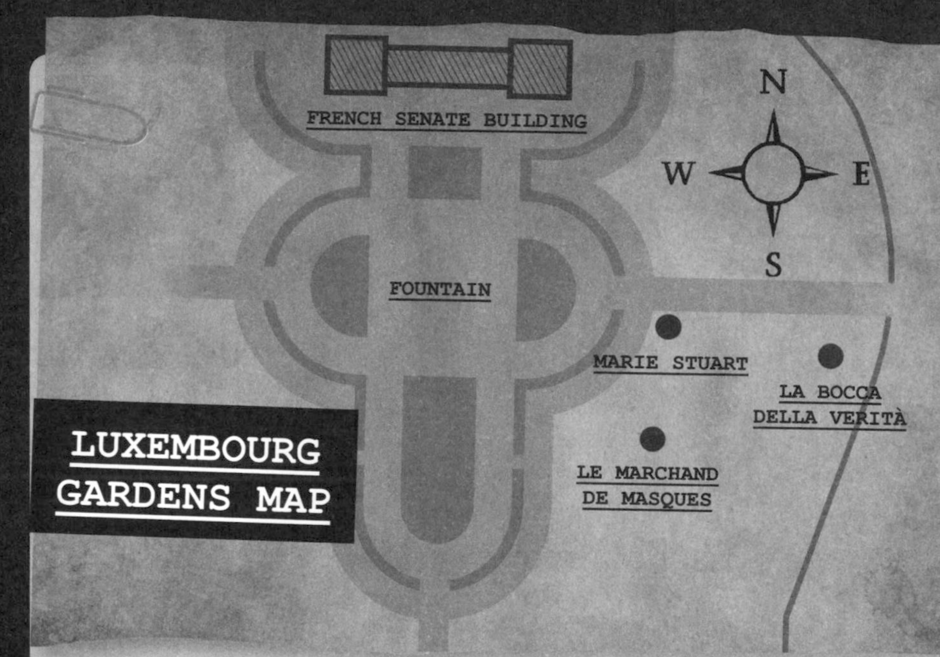

This mission requires you to navigate around a park filled with so many statues it resembles an outdoor museum. Everywhere you turn, it's as if you find another statue watching you. Examine the map, and use it to locate these statues.

LE MARCHAND DE MASQUES

("Luh mar-shand duh mahsk") (The Mask Merchant)

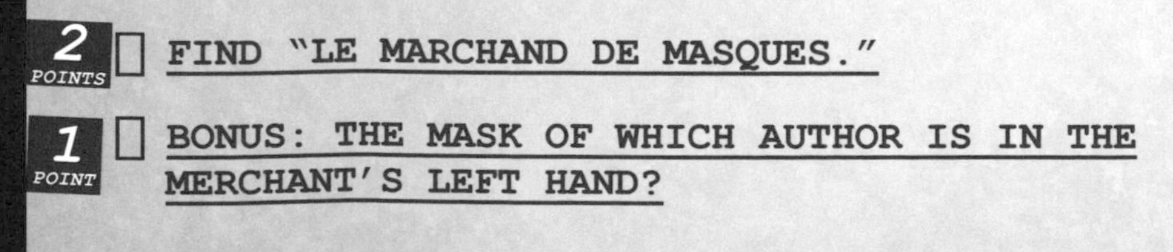

2 POINTS ☐ **FIND "LE MARCHAND DE MASQUES."**

1 POINT ☐ **BONUS: THE MASK OF WHICH AUTHOR IS IN THE MERCHANT'S LEFT HAND?**

7

- LE MARCHAND DE MASQUES STATUE
- MASK OF FRENCH AUTHOR
- MARIE STUART STATUE
- LA BOCCA DELLA VERITÀ STATUE

TOTAL POINTS

Take a look at the masks surrounding the base of the statue. These are the faces of some of France's most famous writers, artists, and musicians peering back at you. Before sly thieves came along, three more masks hung from the merchant's right wrist.

Now the poor merchant only holds a mask in his left hand: it's the mask of a famous French author. Maybe you've heard of some of his novels:

The Hunchback of Notre Dame and *Les Misérables.*

MARIE STUART

(a.k.a Mary Stuart, a.k.a. Mary Queen of Scots)

(A.k.a. stands for "also known as." It's a common term that agents use to identify people who have more than one name.)

☐ **TRACK DOWN THE STATUE OF MARIE STUART.**

See the statue's photo on the next page.

my notes:

In the 1500's England's Queen Elizabeth lived in constant fear of plots to overthrow and assassinate her. Elizabeth had her suspicions about this woman, Mary Stuart, an ambitious woman who believed she should rule over England, due to her royal family ties.

MARY HAD ALREADY SERVED AS QUEEN OF TWO NATIONS- SCOTLAND AND FRANCE. SHE BECAME QUEEN OF SCOTLAND WHEN SHE WAS ONLY SIX DAYS OLD. (HER FATHER, THE KING OF SCOTLAND, DIED WHEN MARY WAS BORN, MAKING HER THE QUEEN.) LATER, SHE RULED FRANCE AS A TEENAGER, UNTIL HER FRENCH HUSBAND, KING FRANCIS, DIED…OF AN EAR INFECTION.

To prevent Mary's dreams of ruling a third nation from coming true, Elizabeth had Mary locked up. Then the queen's spymaster, Francis Walsingham, dispatched a spy to uncover intel on Mary's plan for overthrowing Elizabeth. Walsingham's agent got a hold of encoded messages secretly sent between Mary and her supporters that outlined a plot to do away with the queen. Walsingham decoded the encrypted messages (encrypted means written in a secret code) and showed them to Elizabeth. Mary was sentenced to death by beheading even though questions remained about her involvement in the plot.

LA BOCCA DELLA VERITÀ

(The Mouth of Truth)

☐ **LOCATE "LA BOCCA DELLA VERITÀ" STATUE.**

2 POINTS

Any idea why this girl has a bit of a smile? The sculpture tells the story of an old Roman legend about lying. The mouth in the statue is "the mouth of truth," a sort of old-fashioned lie detector.

Legend has it that if you've lied and you put your hand in the "mouth of truth," then the mouth would bite off your hand. She's not so sure if she wants to take a chance.

Could you remove your hand from the mouth of truth…or would the mouth enjoy it as a snack?

Mary Stuart, Queen Elizabeth, Francis Walsingham

mission: #11 date:___________

SACRÉ COEUR

(Sacré Coeur = "Sak-ray Kuhr")

Congratulations, you've reached Paris' highest point, site of the white-domed church of Sacré Coeur ("Sacred Heart" in English).

THE BASILICA KEEPS ITS WHITE COLOR, THANKS TO THE TRAVERTINE STONE USED TO BUILD IT. THIS SPECIAL STONE PRODUCES A MINERAL CALLED CALCITE THAT KEEPS THE CHURCH WHITE, DESPITE WEATHERING AND THE BIG-CITY POLLUTION.

OUTSIDE

Track down the statue of a French saint, Joan of Arc, a teenager who bravely led the French army to victory against the British. Mounted gallantly atop her horse, she holds a huge battle sword in her hand as if to say, "Charge!" A statue of King Louis IX, holding a crown of thorns, also stands outside. See his story on page 52.

☐ **FIND THE SAINT JOAN OF ARC STATUE.**

10

TOTAL POINTS

- JOAN OF ARC STATUE
- MOSAIC
- SAINT PETER STATUE

INSIDE

Keep your head up, and find the mosaic showing Christ's golden "sacred heart" ("Sacré Coeur"). A "mosaic" is a picture made of small pieces of colored glass or colored stone.

☐ **EXAMINE THE MOSAIC CAREFULLY TO UNCOVER THESE.**

2 POINTS EACH

- **JESUS' SACRED HEART**
- **A GLOBE**
- **SAINT JOAN OF ARC** (to the right of Jesus, with a sword hanging from her waist)

☐ **FINALLY, HUNT DOWN THE STATUE OF SAINT PETER.**

This statue has a bronze foot that has been polished to a shine by many tourists. As so many others have done before, rub St. Peter's bronze foot for good luck and make a wish.

CHÂTEAU DE VINCENNES

(Château de Vincennes = "Sha-toe duh Vahn-sen")

A "CHÂTEAU" IS A "CASTLE," SO CHÂTEAU DE VINCENNES MEANS VINCENNES CASTLE.

France's King Philip VI (VI=6) feared for his life while living in Paris. Too many people wanted to say "au revoir" ("goodbye") to Philip as king. Instead of residing in the city like previous kings, Philip escaped to a mighty castle just outside the city to protect himself from his enemies. Look around the Château de Vincennes and you'll discover all the markings of a strong, defensive castle: a wide moat, thick, massive walls, and a tall, rock-solid tower (called a "keep").

2 POINTS ☐ **LOCATE EACH OF THESE STRUCTURES THAT PROTECTED THE CHÂTEAU FROM ENEMY ATTACK:**

- **THE MOAT** (no longer filled with water, but with lots of grass)
- **THE FORTIFIED WALL**
- **THE KEEP**
- **THE DRAWBRIDGE OVER THE MOAT**

- THE CASTLE'S MOAT, FORTIFIED WALL, KEEP, DRAWBRIDGE
- THE DRAWBRIDGE'S FLEUR-DE-LYS, CROWN, CLOCK
- ARROW SLITS
- PRISONER "GRAFFITI"

TOTAL POINTS

☐ **AT THE DRAWBRIDGE, FIND THESE THINGS ON THE WALLS ABOVE THE ENTRANCE:**

2 *POINTS*

- **FLEUR-DE-LYS** ("flur-duh-lees" lily flowers, the royal symbols of France)
- **A CROWN**
- **A CLOCK**

Make your way to the outside of the keep.

☐ **FROM HERE LOOK UP AND UNCOVER THE ARROW SLITS.**

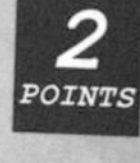

From inside the tower, the king's soldiers would use these thin slits to shoot arrows at any invaders. Castle soldiers loved these. They were easy to shoot an arrow from and almost impossible for the enemy to shoot an arrow into.

The castle also served as a prison.
While inside the castle's tower, examine the walls closely and hunt for the remains of "graffiti" left hundreds of years ago by the prison's inmates. (The "graffiti" you're looking for appears more like faded paintings than today's spray-painted designs.) See the above photos.

☐ **FIND:**

2 *POINTS*

- **RED CURTAINS**
- **THE CHURCH WITH DOMES AND CROSSES**

mission: #13 date: ___________

TOTAL POINTS

CITÉ DES ENFANTS

(Cité des Enfants = "See-tay days Ahn-fahn")

REMEMBER A KEY RULE OF SPYING: THINGS ARE NOT ALWAYS AS THEY SEEM. PIECES OF INTELLIGENCE, LIKE PHOTOS, CAN EASILY BE ALTERED IN ORDER TO DECEIVE YOU.

Examine this photo of *"La Géode" ("Lah Jay-ode")*, a large mirrored sphere at the Cité des Enfants. Judging from it, you'd think the sphere could fit in the palm of your hand. However, once you discover "La Géode," you'll find that's definitely not the case.

3 POINTS ☐ **FIND LA GÉODE. THEN, HAVE SOMEONE ON YOUR TEAM TAKE A SIMILAR PHOTO SO THAT IT APPEARS "LA GÉODE" IS RESTING IN YOUR HAND.**

(Face the sphere, hold out your left hand so your palm faces up and just under the sphere. Cup your hand, then turn to the side. Have your photographer adjust your hand so it looks like the photo.)

mission: #14 date:__________

7

TOTAL POINTS

POMPIDOU CENTER

(Pompidou = "Pom-pee-du")

ALL KINDS OF INTERESTING MODERN ART FILLS THE INSIDE OF THIS MUSEUM, BUT YOUR MISSION TAKES PLACE IN THE OUTDOOR SQUARE.

The design of this museum differs from almost all other buildings. It's like a structure turned inside out. The museum's pipes, tunnels, elevators and escalators are on the building's outside, not the inside. The museum's architect assigned each type a color code:

BLUE = A/C, HEAT
GREEN = PLUMBING
YELLOW = ELECTRICITY
RED = ELEVATORS, ESCALATORS

3 POINTS

☐ **FIND EACH TYPE.**

1 POINT EACH

☐ **LOCATE THESE SCULPTURES IN THE FOUNTAINS IN FRONT OF THE MUSEUM.**

- **THE LIPS**
- **THE SNAKE**
- **THE MERMAID**
- **THE ELEPHANT**

SAINTE CHAPELLE

(Sainte Chapelle = "Sant Sha-pell")

LOUIS IX

ONE OF THE MOST IMPORTANT LESSONS OF SPYING: DON'T TRUST APPEARANCES.

From the outside the Sainte Chapelle ('Holy Chapel' in English) appears rather plain-looking. However, this outside conceals an inside that almost appears to glow - thanks to all the stained glass windows.

King Louis IX (IX = 9) built this place as a lavish shrine to house the Crown of Thorns Jesus had worn upon his head when he was crucified. The Crown had been passed around so many times before Louis got his hands on it in the late 1200's that some wonder, even today, if it was truly the real deal. However, Louis was so confident that he dished out **around $600 million in today's money** for the Crown. (Today the Crown rests in Notre Dame and is displayed on special occasions.)

13

TOTAL POINTS

- FLEUR DE LYS & CASTLES
- KING LOUIS STATUE

Louis became King of France when he was only 12. As he was not quite old enough to lead a kingdom, his mother, Blanche of Castile, ruled until he came of age. Explore the chapel and uncover reminders of both Louis and his mother:

- the fleur-de-lys *("flur-duh-lee")* (lily flower): a symbol of royalty
- the castle: Louis' mother's symbol (Castile = Land of Castles)

☐ **TRACK DOWN EACH OF THESE SIX FLEUR-DE-LYS AND CASTLE DESIGNS (1 POINT FOR EACH TYPE).** 1 POINT EACH

☐ **BONUS: 1 POINT FOR ANY OTHER TYPES OF FLEUR-DE-LYS AND CASTLES YOU FIND. (5 POINTS MAX)** 1 POINT EACH

2 POINTS

☐ **UNCOVER THE KING LOUIS IX STATUE.**

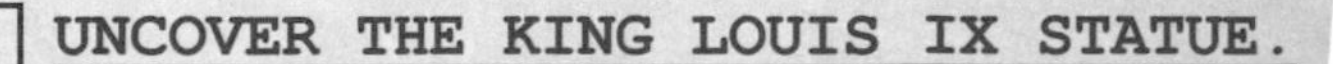

MUSÉE D'ORSAY

(Musée d'Orsay = "Muezay Doorsay")

OUTSIDE

In days past, the structure before you served as a grand train station and elegant hotel. France's P&O Railway operated the station. Two giant clocks decorated the front, which helped ensure passengers made it to their trains on time. These clocks still tick away today, and beneath them you'll find what P&O stands for (two cities in France).

2 POINTS ☐ **WHAT ARE THE CITIES?**

Beneath the clocks you'll find a row containing names of French cities (various stops of the P&O Railway).

1 POINT ☐ **BONUS: FIND THE "O" CITY OF "P&O" HERE.**

INSIDE

Before venturing into the exhibits, stake out a gift shop postcard rack of the museum's works. **Together with your case officer, select a few postcards of interesting items to track down inside.** Your case officer sets the number of points per postcard.

POINT(S) EACH

TOTAL POINTS

- P&O CITIES
- BONUS CITY
- POSTCARD HUNT
- STATUE OF LIBERTY MODEL
- CLOCK WITH A CITY VIEW
- PAINTING HUNT

☐ **FIND THE STATUE OF LIBERTY MODEL.**

2 *POINTS*

The statue's sculptor, Auguste Bartholdi *("Aw-goost Bar-tole-dee")* also designed the original Statue of Liberty, a gift from France to celebrate the 100th anniversary of America's independence.

☐ **FIND A CLOCK WITH A CITY VIEW.**

2 *POINTS*

Stay on point and uncover the below items in paintings. (Examples are included, however you don't necessarily have to find the paintings provided in the examples.)
1 point each, 10 points max

1 *POINT EACH*

☐ **MAN WITH A TOP HAT**

☐ **PERSON DRESSED IN BLACK** (She/He must be the only person in the painting.)

☐ **BALLET DANCER**

☐ **SAILBOAT**

☐ **NIGHT SCENE**

☐ **SNOWY SCENE**

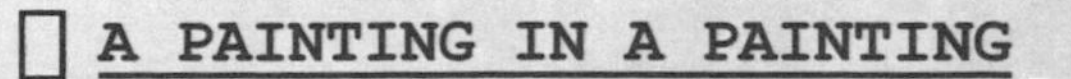

☐ **A PAINTING IN A PAINTING**

my notes:

ANYTIME MISSIONS

THE BEST AGENTS HAVE A HIGH LEVEL OF SOMETHING CALLED "SITUATIONAL AWARENESS." THESE QUICK-WITTED AGENTS PAY CLOSE ATTENTION TO THEIR SURROUNDINGS - READY TO COLLECT CRITICAL INTELLIGENCE AND RESPOND TO DANGEROUS SITUATIONS. HAVING EXCELLENT "SITUATIONAL AWARENESS" (SA FOR SHORT) MEANS ALWAYS BEING "ON ALERT."

These missions will test your SA.

Don't let your guard down as you wander around Paris, or you may miss a chance to win points.

1 POINT EACH

CAROUSELS

Paris has over 30 carousels.

☐ **ONE POINT FOR EACH CAROUSEL YOU FIND.**

(3 points max)

It's your case officer's call whether you may stop and ride on it.

TOTAL POINTS

- CAROUSELS
- STREET MUSICIANS
- SPEAKING FRENCH
- PARISIAN POOCHES
- SAINTS' SIGNS
- FRENCH FOOD: BAKERY, ICE CREAM, CRÊPE

STREET MUSICIANS

It's hard to miss Paris' street musicians. They serenade you on the sidewalk as you trek from one monument to the next, and their tunes mesmerize you in the subway as you wait for your train.

☐ **ONE POINT FOR EACH STREET MUSICIAN YOU SPOT.**

(3 points max)

1 POINT EACH

To receive each point, you must also name the instrument played.

SPEAKING FRENCH

Agents must speak foreign languages to blend in wherever their missions take them. Below you'll find situations to test your French.

☐ **EARN ONE POINT EACH TIME YOU SAY ONE OF THESE FRENCH PHRASES TO A DIFFERENT FRENCH PERSON.** (3 points max)

1 POINT EACH

-When visiting a monument, say hello to a monument staff member:
"Bonjour, Madame" or "Bonjour, Monsieur"
-At a restaurant, a bakery or a food shop, greet the person serving your food by saying:
"Bonjour, Madame" or "Bonjour, Monsieur"
-After you're given the food, thank the person by saying:
"Merci, Madame" or "Merci, Monsieur"

HELLO = BONJOUR = *"BOHN-JOOR"* THANK YOU = MERCI = *"MARE-SEE"*

MA'AM = MADAME = *"MAH-DAHM"* SIR = MONSIEUR = *"MEE-SYUH"*

PARISIAN POOCHES

Walking along the streets of Paris requires you to always be on the lookout. Not only because of your missions, but because you'll need to keep your shoes clean. Why? There's a good chance you will find... piles of dog poop in the middle of Paris' sidewalks. Thousands of dogs walk the sidewalks each day, and their owners don't always pick up after them. Some parts of Paris have even installed street cameras to catch the lazy owners, but the messy problem persists.

People give dogs the royal treatment in Paris. The city has special doggie spas, and canines are even allowed in restaurants.

1 POINT

☐ **ONE POINT FOR SPOTTING A DOG IN A RESTAURANT.**

(And if you see any dog poop on the sidewalk, make sure to avoid it!)

SAINTS' SIGNS

Paris is filled with streets and plazas named after saints, for instance, the Boulevard Saint Michel or the Place Sainte Catherine. Saints were people officially recognized by the church for their holiness and their good works.

☐ **ONE POINT FOR EACH "SAINT" STREET SIGN YOU FIND.** (3 points max)

1 POINT EACH

You can get points for a sign with "rue" *("roo")* (road), "quai" *("kay")* (quay or wharf), "place" *("plas")* (square), "boulevard" *("boo-luh-var")* and "avenue". You'll see signs with "Saint" (a male saint) and "Sainte" (a female saint).

ANYTIME MISSIONS: BONUS

Come across a monument or exhibit that's closed or a line that's just too long? Not enough time in Paris to reach 100 points? Have no fear, use this mission to achieve your goal. Your case officer sets the points.

FRENCH FOOD

To properly blend in, you'll need to eat French food. In a foreign country nothing blows your cover more than eating only cheeseburgers and chicken nuggets.

☐ **At a bakery try buttery croissants** *("kwah-sohn")* **or yummy pain au chocolat** *("pahn O shoko-lah")* **(bread filled with chocolate), brioche** *("bree-O-sh")* **(sweet, fluffy bread), tartes aux fruits** *("tart O frwee")* **(fruit tarts), or some other sweet treat.**

_____ *POINT(S) EACH*

☐ **Try some of the best ice cream ever - Berthillon** *("Bare-tee-ohn")*.

_____ *POINT(S) EACH*

☐ **Eat a delicious crêpe** *("crep")*. **Similar to very thin pancakes, these come with tasty fillings like Nutella (a chocolate spread), fruit, and whipped cream. You can watch street vendors make yours to order. They spread the dough over a hot griddle, top it with your choice of fillings, roll it up, and hand it over for you to enjoy. (Careful, sometimes they're hot!)**

_____ *POINT(S) EACH*

ONCE A FINAL ANSWER IS SUBMITTED, YOUR CASE OFFICER CAN CHECK IT HERE.

IF YOU PEEK AT THIS ANSWER KEY BEFORE SUBMITTING YOUR FINAL ANSWER, YOU WON'T RECEIVE ANY POINTS FOR THAT QUESTION.

MOST MISSIONS DO NOT HAVE ONE CORRECT ANSWER.
FOR THOSE THAT DO, HERE ARE THE ANSWERS.

Pre-Arrival Brief:

A: Sacré Coeur, B: Eiffel Tower, C: Arc de Triomphe, D: Notre Dame

Missions in Paris:

#1 Notre Dame:

-The front: There are 28 biblical kings (the Kings of Judah).
-Inside: There are three rose windows. The number of colors in them is virtually as many colors as your imagination allows. (Four points maximum for the colors though.)

#3 Louvre:

-Glass pyramids: There are five glass pyramids (four outside, one inside that's upside down).
-Egyptian art: A sphinx has the body of a lion.
-Mesopotamia: Shedus/Lamassus have wings. They have five legs.
-The Wedding Feast at Cana: The animals include birds, dogs, and a cat. A dog is standing on the table.
-Items added to 'The Cheat': A diamond on the card behind the man's back, a dark blue tassel on this man's shoulder, an earring on the woman who's standing, a gold coin to the left of the woman seated, a "bracelet" on the man on the right.
-Items added to 'Autumn': a red flower on the right border (center), a small potato under the dark grapes of the man's "hair", a second green apple on the man's "neck", a small red apple in the lower left corner to the right of the red flower, a beige flower in the lower right corner.

#6 Champs-Élysées:

-The top of the obelisk is gold.

#8 Eiffel Tower:

-The man is Thomas Edison.

#10 Luxembourg Gardens:

-The Mask Merchant: The author is Victor Hugo.

#16 Musée d'Orsay

-The two cities: Paris and Orléans.

Note: The information in this book was accurate as of April 2014. We hope that you won't find anything outdated related to the clues. If you do find that something has changed, please email us to kindly let us know.

info@ScavengerHuntAdventures.com

THE FINAL MISSION

"I'm Joining Today!"

Case officers, please visit
scavengerhuntadventures.com/bonus
(all lowercase letters)

☐ **JOIN 'THE INSIDER' (OUR EMAIL LIST)**
You'll get a special bonus mission for this city plus our free e-book, *The Museum Spy.*

PLEASE HELP SPREAD THE WORD

"We'd Love To Help!"

We're a small family business and would be thrilled if you **left a review online*** or **recommended our books to a friend.**

Our books: Paris, London, Amsterdam, Rome, NYC, D.C., Barcelona, Florence, St. Augustine, with more coming!

*We can't mention the site name here, but it begins with "AM"!

A BIG THANK YOU

Thank you for supporting our family-owned business.
Mom writes, Dad serves in the military, Grandma is VP of Logistics and Jr. helps research our books. **Without you this series wouldn't be possible.**

Thank YOU!

Catherine

IMAGE CREDITS: Note- the two digit numbers are the file license number (links below), links to the photographer sites are below. *T=Top, B=Bottom, L=Left, R=Right, C=Center;* From Wikimedia:p.4:TL-Newsinteratlas-2.5;TR-David.Monniaux-2.5;BL- Milliped-3.0;BR-Newsinteratlas-2.5; p.5:LL-Fastily-2.5;RC-Christophe Finot,2.5; p.6:TC-Fastily-2.5;BL-Mossot-3.0;BR-Brown Univ. p.7:Socosi-3.0; p.8:L-Freedom Wizard-3.0;R-Coentor-3.0;p.9:BL-Terrazzo,2.0;BC-Christophe Finot,2.5;BR-Charles Marville; p.10:BL-Loic LLH-3.0;BR-Martie Swartz-3.0; p.11:Axel Boldt;p.12:TL-Popular Science Monthly,TR-Unknown; p.13-T-Julie Ann Workman-3.0, B-French National Archives; p.14:T-Louis Bretez/Claude Lucas;BR-Jastrow; p.15: National Gallery; p.17:SirenCom-3.0; p.19:TC-Louis Bretez/Claude Lucas; BC-Jurgen Haug-3.0; p.20:BL-C.J.-3.0;BR-E. Michael Smith; p.21: T-TR James-3.0;B-Poulpy-3.0;p.22-27:Wikimedia;p.28:"H"- Jastrow; TR-Versailles Palace;BR-Jastrow (photo of painting); p.29: Mu-3.0 p.30 R-Carl Purcell;L-David Monniaux-2.5; p.31:T-Jebulon 1.0;BL-David.Monniaux-2.5; p.32:L-Tristan Nitot-3.0;R-Coralive-3.0; p.36:R-Felix Nadar;L-Unknown;p.37:L-Fastily-2.5;p.38:L-Djtox-3.0;R-Brown University;p.39;p.40:Rigg Welter-2.5;p.41:Library of Congress;p.43-44:Tosca-3.0;p.45:Marc Baronnet-3.0, portraits-National Portrait Gallery; p.46:L-Christophe Finot,2.5;R-Casss-3.0;p.47:Didier B-2.5; p.48:L-Chatsam-3.0,R-Garitan-3.0; p.49:L-Vassil;R-Chatsam;p.52: TR- Musee Conde, BR-Louvre;p. 53: LL,LC,CR-Benjamin Nunez Gonzalez-3.0;B-PHGCOM-3.0; Musee d'Orsay left page: BR-Wikifrosh-3.0; right page, Bartholid: Smithsonian; Anytime Missions: Musician-The Super,Ice cream-Lotus Head; From Flickr (all licensed under 2.0 unless otherwise noted): p.5:CL-Terrazzo;RR-Jiugang Wang;p.8:B-Wisegie; p.10:T-Serge Melki; p.14:BL-Chris Yunker; p.16:Jean-Francois Gornet; p.18:Leon Brocard;p.31-Terrazzo;p.33:B-Fabio Venni;p.37:R-Jiugang Wang;p.39:Josua Michealis; p.51:T-Alife Ianni;B-Dave Hamster; Sainte Chapelle, left page: L-CJuneau; right page:center two-Bruce Reyes Chow;RR-Randy Connolly; Musee d'Orsay left page: T-Joe DeSousa;right page: Derek Key; Anytime Missions: Carousel-Lorena Suarez,Dog-Josiah Mackenzie,Flag-Wisegie,Bakery-Yisris
Flickr User Website Link Example: http://www.flickr.com/photos/79865753@N00 = photos/79865753@N00:
Terrazzo: photos/terrazzo/; Jiugang Wang: people/32366606@N00; Wisegie: photos/whizzer/; Serge Melki:people/67958110@N00; Chris Yunker: photos/chris-yunker/;Jean Francois Gornet: photos/jfgornet/;Leon Brocard: photos/35034350386@N01;Lorena Suarez: people/13694964@N00;In Sappho We Trust: photos/skinnylawyer/;
Patrick Janicek: photos/marsupilami92/;Randy Connolly: photos/randyconnolly/;Bruce Reyes Chow: photos/reyes-chow/;Joe DeSousa: photos/mustangjoe/;Derek Key: people/32211216@N06;Cjuneau: photos/15558406@N03/;
Alfie Ianni: photos/ainet/;Dave Hamster: photos/davehamster/;Josiah Mackenzie: photos/josiahmackenzie/; Links to Licenses: 2.0: http://creativecommons.org/licenses/by-sa/2.0/deed.en; 2.5: http://creativecommons.org/licenses/by-sa/2.5/deed.en; 3.0: http://creativecommons.org/licenses/by-sa/3.0/deed.en

www.ScavengerHuntAdventures.com